A Rainbow a Day...

Over **30** crafts and activities to make you smile!

Published in the UK by Scholastic Children's Books, 2020

Euston House, 24 Eversholt Street, London, NW1 1DB

A division of Scholastic Limited

London – New York – Toronto – Sydney - Auckland

Mexico City – New Delhi – Hong Kong

SCHOLASTIC and associated logos are trademarks and/or

registered trademarks of Scholastic Inc.

Cover design by Claire Yeo © Scholastic Children's Books, 2020

Text © Scholastic Children's Books, 2020

Content originally published in:

The Great British Activity Book (2013), 978 1407 13616 5

My Beautiful Unicorn (2016), 978 1407 16823 4

Magical Poopy Surprise (2019), 978 1407 19578 0

My Mini Unicorn Journal (2019), 978 1407 18956 7

Image credits: pp22–3 & pp64–5: © Cloud King Creative.

ISBN 978 0702 30576 4

A CIP catalogue record for this book is available from the British Library.

Printed in the UK by Bell and Bain Ltd, Glasgow

Papers used by Scholastic Children's Books are made from wood grown in sustainable forests.

1 3 5 7 9 10 8 6 4 2

www.scholastic.co.uk

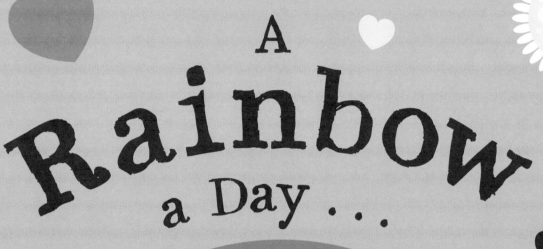

A Rainbow a Day . . .

. . . keeps the grey clouds away!

Grab your rainbow-coloured pens or pencils to brighten up this book!

■ SCHOLASTIC

Ready, Set, RAINBOW!

You will need:

* A group of family members
* Something to collect your finds in
* Something to time yourself with
* Someone to act as the judge

How to play:

This rainbow scavenger hunt is best played outside, but you can play inside too. The aim of the game is to gather the best items in each of the colours of the rainbow. The person with the most interesting and varied finds wins.

✿ BUT BE QUICK, YOU'VE ONLY GOT HALF AN HOUR TO DO IT IN. WHAT WILL YOU DISCOVER?

The colours of the rainbow are:
red, orange, yellow, green, blue, indigo and violet.

My Rainbow Items:

Red: ....

Orange: ....

Yellow: ....

Green: ....

Blue: ....

Indigo: ....

Violet: ....

Remember to only take items you don't think anyone will mind you taking. And if you do use something belonging to someone else, make sure you ask them first!

Rainbow Cookies

Bake these beautiful, bright biscuits to share with your family.
Make sure you ask an adult to help you!

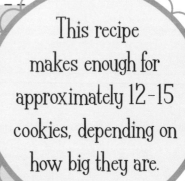

This recipe makes enough for approximately 12-15 cookies, depending on how big they are.

You will need:

* 225g butter

* 100g caster sugar

* 200g brown sugar

* 1 teaspoon vanilla extract

* 2 eggs

* 350g Smarties (or any other brightly coloured chocolate)

* 350g plain flour

* 1 teaspoon bicarbonate of soda

* 1 teaspoon of salt

How to make them:

1. Ask an adult to preheat your oven to 190°C/375°F/gas mark 5.

2. In a large bowl, combine the butter, caster sugar, brown sugar and vanilla extract. Stir until this is light and fluffy, then beat in the eggs.

3. Weigh out your flour into a medium-sized bowl and combine it with the bicarbonate of soda and salt. Then fold it into your sugar and butter mixture. Finally, add in your coloured chocolate and stir. You've now made your cookie dough!

4. Start taking small amounts of dough and rolling it into balls. Place the balls on two baking trays with lots of space between them. Bake them for 10-12 minutes, depending on how gooey you like them.

5. Leave them to cool on the baking trays (or on a wire rack), then share with friends.

Delicious!

Brighten Your Day!

Fill these pages with the brightest doodles and scribbles,
and the happiest words you can think of!

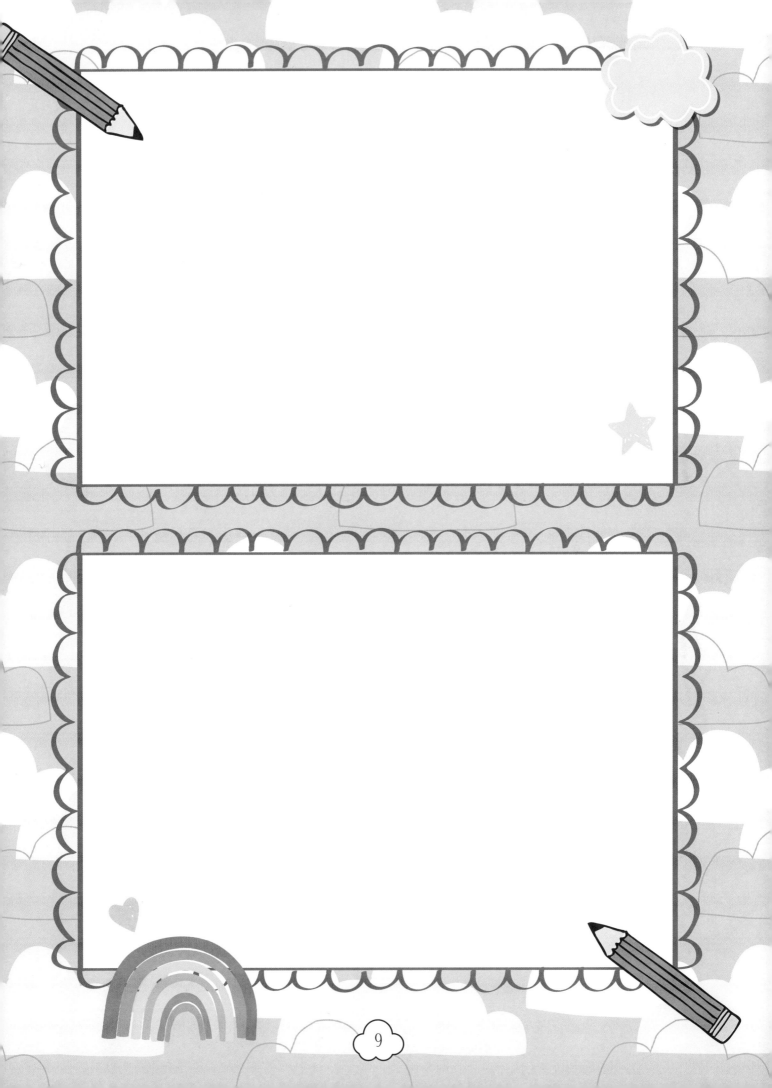

Rainbow Friendship Bracelets

Learn how to make these colourful bracelets –
they will brighten anyone's day!

You will need:

* Thread in three colours of the rainbow

* Scissors

Remember to ask an adult to help you when using scissors.

How to make them:

1. Choose thread in your favourite colours. Measure and cut the strands. Each strand should be about the same length as your shoulder to your fingertips.

2. Tie them together in a knot at the end. Pin or tape the end to a stable surface. Spread out the individual strands.

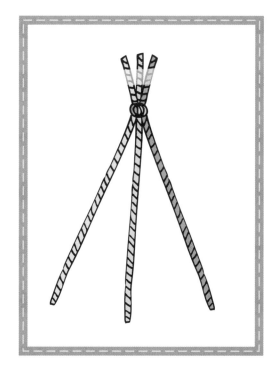

3. Knot the far-left thread to the next thread along. To do this, take the left thread over the top of the second thread, as shown here.

4. Then pull the first thread under the second, and up through the loop until the knot moves up to the top of the second thread. Hold the second thread tightly so the knot pulls tight.

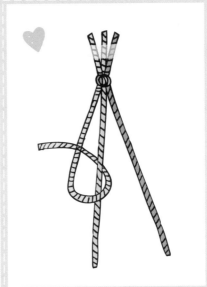

5. Repeat this knot again with the same two threads.

6. Take the same thread as before and repeat the knots around the next thread along. Now take the next thread and repeat steps 3-6.

7. Continue knotting the far-left thread around the other threads from left to right. Each time, this thread will end up on the far right.

8. Keep going until the bracelet fits your wrist.

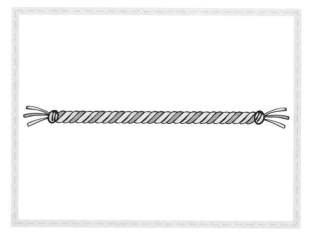

9. Tie a knot in the end. Trim any excess thread. Tie the two ends of the friendship bracelet together around your friend's wrist. You're finished! Now help your friend make a matching one for you.

Float Away!

Up, up and away!
Colour these balloons in rainbow colours.

A Really Rainbow Poem

An acrostic poem is a fun poem in which the first letters of each line spell out a word or phrase. The poem doesn't need to rhyme and the lines can be a single word or a whole sentence - it's up to you!

R ed jelly

A nd

I ndigo ice cream

N eeds some

B iscuity

O range

W afers on top!

R
A
I
N
B
O
W

Now choose any word you like
and write a second poem.
You could spell out your name or a friend's.

Glitterati Party Slime

If you need a bit of glitz in your day, this could be the goo
for you! It's super-quick to make, too.

You will need:

* 125 ml clear PVA glue or glitter glue

* 30 ml water

* 1/2 tsp bicarbonate of soda

* contact lens solution

* glitter - iridescent ones are so sparkly!

1

Pour the glue and water
into a bowl and mix.
You can skip step 3 if
you use glitter glue!

2

Add the bicarbonate of
soda and mix until it
has dissolved.

3

Choose your favourite shade of glitter, or mix in two colours together for extra sparkle.

4

Next, add squirts of contact lens solution, mixing as you go.

5

Stretch and knead your glitter slime until it is the perfect consistency.

Tip to Try!
Add acrylic paint or food colouring to give your slime a splash of colour!

Sweet and Savoury Rainbows

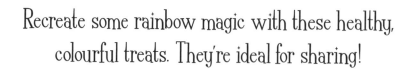

Recreate some rainbow magic with these healthy, colourful treats. They're ideal for sharing!

You will need foods in different colours of the rainbow.
You can use whatever you like, but some suggestions are:

Sweet platter

Red: red apples, strawberries, raspberries

Orange: oranges, satsumas, clementines, apricots, melon

Yellow: bananas, pineapple, mango

Green: green apples, pears, green grapes

Blue/purple: blueberries, blackberries, blackcurrants, plums, red grapes

Savoury platter

Red: red peppers, tomatoes

Orange: orange peppers, carrots

Yellow: yellow pepper, sweetcorn

Green: cucumber, celery, peas in a pod, green pepper

Blue/purple: aubergines, beetroot, courgettes

How to make them:

1. Choose whether you want your rainbow to be sweet or savoury.

2. Ask an adult to help you prepare the food you've chosen. Some of the vegetables might need to be cooked first, and it will all need to be washed and chopped. Don't worry if you haven't managed to find all the colours - just use the ones you have!

3. Once the food is ready, arrange it all on a large plate in order of the colours of the rainbow (red, orange, yellow, green and blue/purple).

Make sure an adult is present for all food chopping.

Puzzle Piece Necklaces

Follow the instructions to make your very
own pair of jigsaw puzzle necklaces.

You will need:

* An old jigsaw puzzle

* A few different coloured paints including white (we recommend
  you use acrylic paints)

* An adult helper who can put a hole in your jigsaw puzzle piece

* Some string or the chain from an old necklace
  (you will need two of these)

How to make it:

1. Find two jigsaw puzzle pieces that slot together. Paint them both in
   whatever way you want to, starting with a thick white base. Use the
   blank spaces on the next page to practise your designs.

2. Ask an adult to carefully put a hole
   in each of your painted jigsaw puzzle
   pieces when they've dried.

3. Thread some string or an old necklace
   chain through each jigsaw puzzle piece.

4. Now wear one and save one for
   a friend or family member!

Depending on the thickness
of your chosen jigsaw piece
you might be able to use a
hole punch to put the holes
in your puzzle pieces
or an adult could use
something sharper.

Practise your jigsaw
pattern designs
in the pieces below:

If you've got a
group of friends, you
can always make more
necklaces using other
pieces of the puzzle that
fit together.

Rainbow Poops!

Draw doodles on these doo-doos, then add some
colour to make the poops look perfect!

Rainbow Power

Doodle patterns and add some rainbow colours to give this unicorn a magical makeover.

23

Share a Smile

A great way to keep in touch with people is
by sending postcards or letters.

Colour in and cut out the postcard templates
on the following pages. You might need to
stick them onto cardboard before posting,
or you could just pop them into an envelope.

Remember to
ask an adult to
help you when
using scissors.

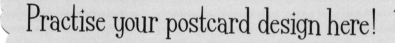

Practise your postcard design here!

To

STAMP
HERE

To

STAMP
HERE

To

STAMP
HERE

To

STAMP
HERE

High in the Sky

Grab your rainbow-coloured pencils and
add some pretty patterns to the kites.

Rainbow Poop Treats

Made with just four ingredients and ready in under an hour, these no-bake unicorn poop treats are so easy to make and healthy, too!

You will need:

* 125 g coconut flour
* 350 g smooth cashew butter*
* 85 g maple syrup
* 1-2 tbsp hundreds and thousands

*IMPORTANT ALLERGY ADVICE:

nut allergy sufferers should replace the cashew butter with sunflower seed butter or biscuit spread.

1

Line a baking tray or chopping board with greaseproof paper and put to one side.

2

Sieve the coconut flour into a large mixing bowl. Add your cashew butter and maple syrup and mix until combined.

3

Next, stir in the hundreds and thousands. If the mixture is too thin, stir in more coconut flour, a spoonful at a time. If the mixture is too thick, add a little milk or water.

4

Using your hands, form small balls. Roll each ball into a sausage shape and make a point at one end.

5

Make each sausage into a poopy pile shape with the point at the top and place on the greaseproof paper.

6

Place the tray in the fridge for at least thirty minutes, or until the treats have firmed up.

YUM!

Jar of Happy

Have you ever wanted to feel as bright as a rainbow? Make your own Jar of Happy and pick a different note to bring a smile to your face each day!

You will need:

* a large jar with a lid

* ribbon or stickers to decorate your jar

* scissors

1 Choose a jar that's large enough to hold your happiness notes.

2 Ask an adult to help you cut out the notes on the opposite page.

3 Fold the notes and pop them in the jar.

4 Add more notes over time – why not write down things that make you happy?

5 Take a note from the jar and read whenever you need a little sparkle in your life!

If at first you don't succeed,
click your heels and try again.

In a field full of horses,
be a unicorn.

Why fit in when you were
born to stand out?

Happiness is a unicorn pooping rainbows.

Do the right thing, even
when no one's watching.

Dream big.

You are 99% rainbow.

Be honest. Be kind.
Be magical.

Make a wish.

You are somebody's reason to smile.

Believe in magic and
you will find it.

Reach for the stars!

Paint the town rainbow.

May all your dreams come true.

Party like a unicorn.

You are smart. You are strong.
You can do anything.

Always be yourself

Believe in your inner unicorn.

You are magical.

You don't need wings to fly.

You're one of a kind,
born to be wild.

Anything is possible.

Whatever you do, have fun.

Make your own magic.

Never stop dreaming.

You can't have a rainbow
without a little rain.

It's going to be a rainbow
kind of day.

Time spent playing is never time wasted.

Unicorns can't fly.
You can't fly... You are a unicorn!

A smile is the best make-up.

Dreams are the playground of unicorns.

You are like a rainbow: bright,
sweet and magical.

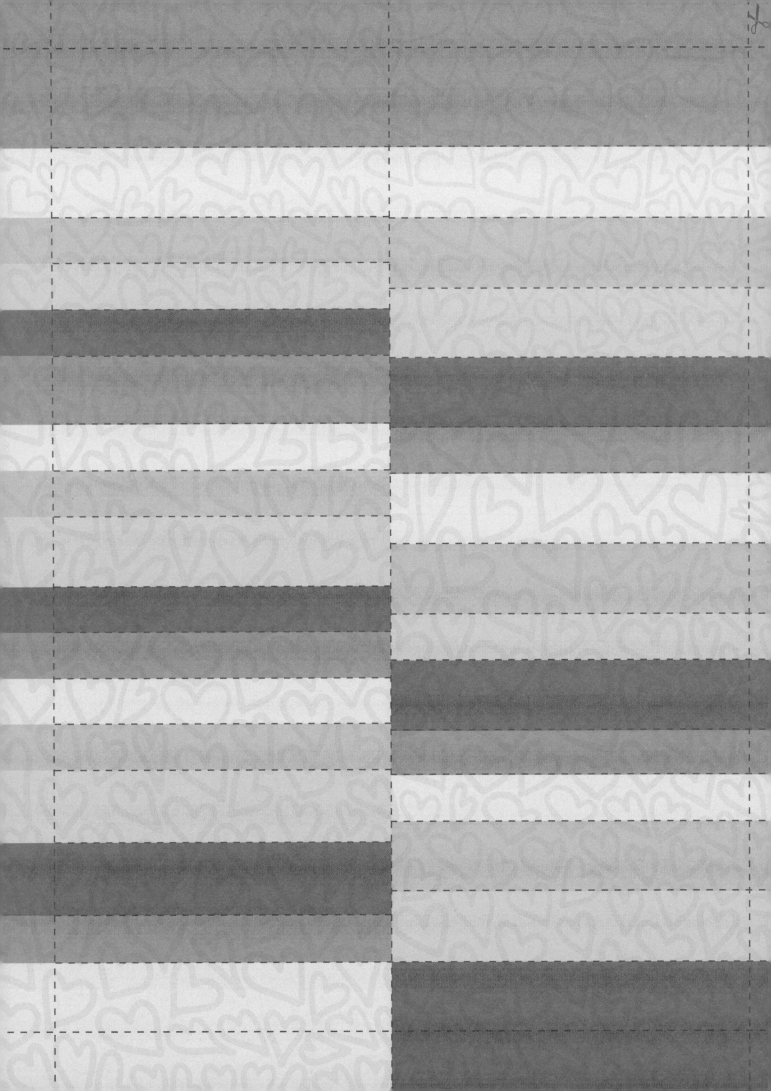

Beautiful Birds

Rainbows, Rainbows, Everywhere...

Fill each picture frame with as many rainbows
and happy words that you can fit in!

Special Stories

Writing is such a fun way to spend an afternoon.
Use the ideas below for inspiration, then start writing.
Maybe you'll become a famous author one day.

Circle the names of three characters:

Jazzie   Lila   Alex   Ariana

Celia   Henry   Jacob   Mia

Circle a setting:

The end of the rainbow

A different planet

Under the sea

A haunted wood

Circle a plot:

A magical object is discovered

A friend goes missing

A hidden door swings open

A friend's secret is revealed

Circle four adjectives to use:

Huge   Cold   Mysterious   Loud

Powerful   Sinister   Special

Glowing   Red   Happy   Sparkly

Fantastical   Shimmering   Jewel-covered

Name of your story:

Write it here:

Quick Draw!

How many mini rainbows can you draw in one minute? Ready, steady ... rainbow!

Rainbow Surprise!

Colour in the shapes using the colour key,
to reveal a sparkly surprise!

R = red

O = orange

Y = yellow

G = green

L = light blue

D = dark blue

P = purple

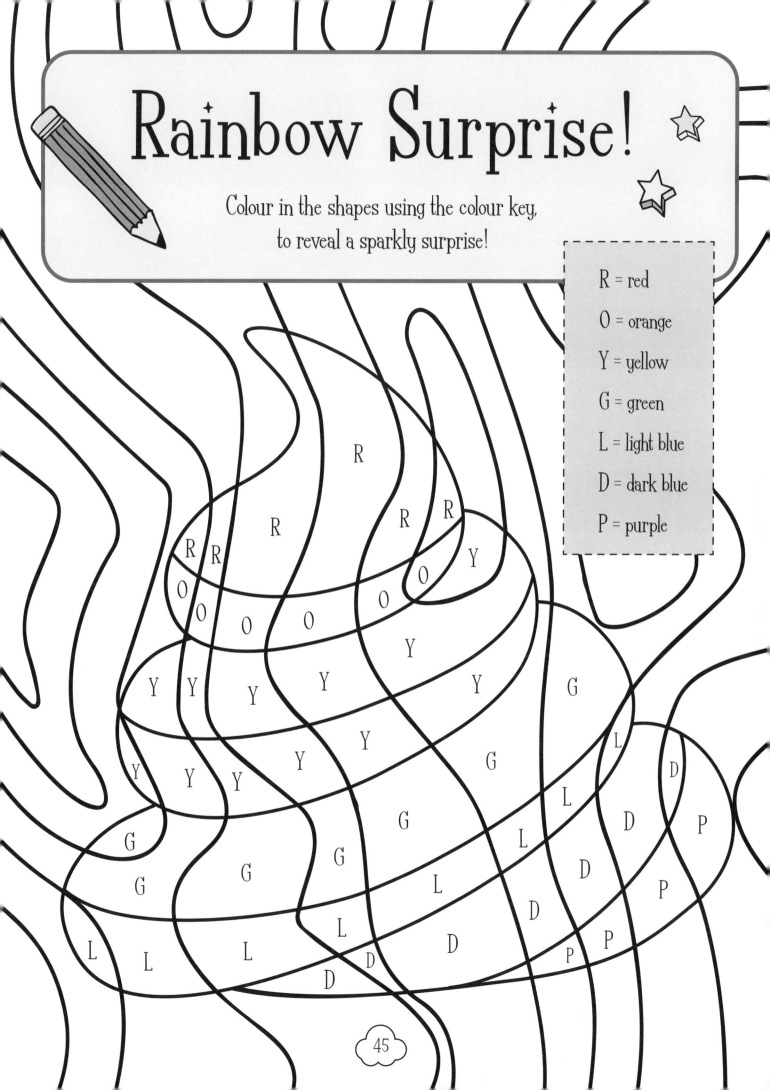

Beautiful Bunting

Colour in this bunting with your brightest pencils!

Rainbow Inspiration

A fun way to get creative is to make a collage. Go through any old magazines or newspapers and cut out images you like, or tear up pieces of brightly coloured paper.

Once you've got a good pile of colourful pieces, simply stick them all down on these blank pages!

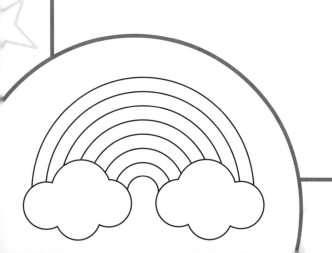

You will need:

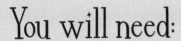

* Colourful pages from magazines or newspapers

* Colourful pieces of paper

* Scissors

* Glue

Remember to ask an adult to help you when using scissors.

Perfect Paperchains

Follow the steps below to create these paperchains.
They're great to decorate your room with!

You will need:

* A4 paper

* Scissors

* A pencil

* Coloured pens or pencils

Remember to ask an adult to help you when using scissors.

How to make them:

1. Cut your piece of A4 paper in half lengthways. This will give you enough paper for two chains.

2. Taking one piece of paper, fold it back and forth (as if you're making a paper fan) until you reach the end.

3. Copy a shape, such as a heart, onto your paper with your pencil. The sides of the shape need to reach the edges of the paper.

4. Cut out your shape.

5. Open up the paper and you should have a shaped paperchain!

6. Colour in the paperchain with your pens or pencils. Then make one with the other half of the A4 paper.

Secret Letter

Use the code below or make up your own to create a secret language only you and your friends will understand.

Then use the next pages to write a message to a friend or keep a note of something you don't want anyone to find out!

Lovely Leaves

Take a quiet moment to colour in these
lovely leaves with bright rainbow colours.

Magical Rainbow Slime

Super-colourful and squishy, this slime combines all the colours of the rainbow! Adding glitter will make your slime more magical still!

You will need:

* 1 large batch of fluffy slime (see page 64 for the recipe)
* food colouring or paint for each rainbow colour
* 7 small containers
* glitter (optional)

Tip to Try!
Take care not to overmix the colours, or your slime may go brown.

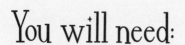

1

Start by making a large batch of white fluffy slime.

Washing your hands after kneading each batch will stop the colours from transferring.

2

Divide up the slime into seven small containers – one for each rainbow colour. Add drops of food colouring or paint to each pot. Knead the colours one at a time, adding more colouring, until you have the shades you want.

3

Roll the colours into long pieces, then press them together, as shown.

4

Now stretch out the colours to create a cool rainbow shape or carefully squish them together.

MIX UP SOME MAGIC!

Rainbow Greetings

Want to surprise a friend or family member? Try making this cute greetings card to bring sparkle to any celebration!

SHINE LIKE A RAINBOW

1 Ask an adult to help you cut out the page, along the vertical line.

2 Fold the card in half along the fold line.

3 Decide which lucky person you're going to send your card to, then write their name and add your autograph.

4 Find an envelope that fits the card and write your friend's name on the envelope.

Have a Magical Day!

SHINE LIKE A RAINBOW

Have a Magical Day!

Get Outside!

If you're bored, then get outside! Sevens is a brilliant game to play with seven steps - one for each colour of the rainbow. You can play by yourself or with someone else. All you need is a small, bouncy ball and a wall to bounce it against. Here's how to play:

1. Stand away from the wall, throw the ball at the wall and catch it.

2. Throw the ball at the wall, but let it bounce before you catch it.

3. Throw the ball at the wall, use your hand to whack it back at the wall, then catch it.

4. Repeat step **3**, but this time let the ball bounce before you catch it.

5. Hit the ball at the wall, let it bounce, whack it back then catch it.

6. Repeat step **5**, but bounce the ball on the ground before you catch it.

7. Lastly, repeat step **6**, but bounce the ball on the ground twice at the end before you catch it.

Try the steps again, but add a twist before you throw. You can:

* Clap your hands * Shout 'rainbow!'
* Spin on the spot * Only use your right hand * Only use your left hand
* Throw the ball under one leg
* Throw the ball under the other leg.

Fluffy Slime Recipe for page 56

You will need:

* 500 ml white or clear PVA glue

* 125 ml shaving foam

* food colouring or acrylic paint

* liquid laundry detergent

How to make it:

1. Pour the glue into a large mixing bowl. Add the shaving foam, gently folding it into the glue.

2. Add laundry detergent, a drop at a time, and mix well. The mixture should begin to come away from the sides of the bowl.

3. Gently knead the slime on a clean work surface until it reaches a slime consistency. Be careful not to work the slime too hard.

Slime Safety

* The slime activities in this book require adult supervision at all times.

* Ingredients may cause skin irritation – we recommend that gloves are worn when making or handling slime and that slime is not handled for prolonged periods of time.

* Always wash your hands and tools with soap and water and disinfect surfaces once you have finished an activity.

* Never eat or taste slime or slime-making ingredients.

* Make sure that slime is kept away from very young children and pets.

* Slime may stain – wear old clothes and cover surfaces to prevent damage.

* If any slime or slime-making ingredients come into contact with your eyes, flush well with water.

* Dispose of slime in a waste container in the dustbin – do not put slime down sinks or drains.

* Slime only has a short shelf life, throw away at the first sign of any mould or odour.

* The publisher shall not be liable or responsible in any respect for any use or application of any information or material contained in this book or any adverse effect, consequence, injury, loss or damage of any type resulting or arising from, directly or indirectly, the use or application of any information or material contained in this book.